Ophthalmic Medical Assisting

An Independent Study Course

Fourth Edition

Examination

600297

AMERICAN ACADEMY OF OPHTHALMOLOGY
The Eye M.D. Association

 **ALLERGAN**

Sponsored in part by an
unrestricted grant from
Allergan, Inc.

AMERICAN ACADEMY
OF OPHTHALMOLOGY
The Eye M.D. Association

655 Beach Street
P.O. Box 7424
San Francisco, CA 94120-7424

Fourth Edition
Authors/Revisers

Emanuel Newmark, MD, FACS (Executive Editor),
    West Palm Beach, Florida
Donna M. Applegate, COT, New Albany, Indiana
Dimitri T. Azar, MD, Boston, Massachusetts
Tyree Carr, MD, FACS, Las Vegas, Nevada
Neil T. Choplin, MD, San Diego, California
Peter C. Donshik, MD, FACS, Bloomfield,
    Connecticut
Lindreth G. DuBois, MEd, MMSc, CO, COMT,
    Atlanta, Georgia
Lee R. Duffner, MD, FACS, Hollywood, Florida
L. Neal Freeman, MD, FACS, Melbourne, Florida
Kate Goldblum, RN, Albuquerque, New Mexico
Elbert H. Magoon, MD, Canton, Ohio
Jeanne H. Nielson, OCS, Salt Lake City, Utah
Mary O'Hara, MD, Davis, California
Clifford Lee Salinger, MD, Palm Beach Gardens,
    Florida
Diana J. Shamis, MHSE, CO, COMT, Gainesville,
    Florida
Charles B. Slonim, MD, FACS, Tampa, Florida
Walter L. Underwood, FACMPE, Atlanta, Georgia
Danne Ventura, COA, FNAO, Redwood City,
    California

Fourth Edition
Reviewers

Donna M. Applegate, COT, New Albany, Indiana
Gregory S. Brinton, MD, Salt Lake City, Utah
Peter C. Donshik, MD, FACS, Bloomfield,
    Connecticut
Lindreth G. DuBois, MEd, MMSc, CO, COMT,
    Atlanta, Georgia
Kate Goldblum, RN, Albuquerque, New Mexico
David R. Hardten, MD, Minneapolis, Minnesota
Karla J. Johns, MD, Nashville, Tennessee
Jacqueline S. Lustgarten, MD, River Edge, New
    Jersey
Elbert H. Magoon, MD, Canton, Ohio
Jeanne H. Nielson, OCS, Salt Lake City, Utah
Mary O'Hara, MD, Davis, California
Tully C. Patrowicz, MD, Eustis, Florida
David Sarraf, MD, Los Angeles, California
Carla J. Siegfried, MD, St. Louis, Missouri
Scott C. Sigler, MD, Oklahoma City, Oklahoma
George A. Stern, MD, Missoula, Montana
William B. Trattler, MD, Miami, Florida

Academy Staff

Richard Zorab, Vice President, Ophthalmic
    Knowledge
Hal Straus, Director of Publications
William M. Hering, PhD, Director of CME,
    Programs, and Acquisitions
Susan R. Keller, Acquisitions Editor
Kimberly Torgerson, Publications Manager
Ruth Modric, Production Manager

ISBN 978-1-56055-599-5

Printed in China

06 5 4 3 2

Ophthalmic Medical Assisting

An Independent Study Course

Fourth Edition

Examination Instructions

This examination is for use only with the fourth edition of *Ophthalmic Medical Assisting: An Independent Study Course.* It comprises 188 multiple-choice test items. Each test item consists of an incomplete statement followed by a choice of four possible completions.

Completing the Examination

For each numbered test item, select the one lettered option that best completes each statement and fill in the corresponding lettered circle on the answer sheet. You may refer to the text *Ophthalmic Medical Assisting, Fourth Edition,* while completing the examination. The correct responses to the test items are based on information provided in the textbook. Even though your practical experience or the policies and practices in your office may differ somewhat from information given in the course textbook, the textbook is the sole source of a correct response for the purposes of this examination.

Mark your answers in this examination booklet as well as on the answer sheet in case your answer sheet is lost or you must repeat the examination. Please do not share your examination booklet, answer sheet, or any other information about the answers with other individuals who may be attempting to complete this course examination. Doing so defeats the instructional purpose and reduces the benefit of this examination for all involved.

Submitting the Answer Sheet for Scoring

Because of the complexity of the text material, the American Academy of Ophthalmology suggests that a student spend at least 3 months mastering the text before submitting a completed examination answer sheet for scoring. The Academy does not guarantee the ability to score an answer sheet submitted more than 2 years after the examination booklet has been purchased.

Remove your completed answer sheet from the booklet by tearing along the perforation, and mail it to the American Academy of Ophthalmology in the envelope that is attached to the examination booklet. If your return envelope is missing, mail your answer sheet, folded according to directions, in a #10 envelope to

American Academy of Ophthalmology
Independent Study Course Examination
P.O. Box 7424
San Francisco, CA 94120-7424

Only the original preprinted serially numbered answer sheet from the examination booklet may be submitted; photocopies cannot be scored. If your serially numbered answer sheet is torn or otherwise damaged, return it to the Academy for a replacement.

Before mailing, check your answer sheet to be sure that you have filled in one—and only one—circle for each test item, that the answer sheet is undamaged and contains no stray marks, and that it is folded correctly for mailing. Check that you have correctly and completely provided all other information requested on both sides of the answer sheet, including your name; the address to which you want your test results mailed; the printed name *and signature* of your Sponsoring Ophthalmologist; and the 6-digit student identification number, located on the title page of the examination booklet and on the back of the answer sheet. An answer sheet without this information cannot be scored.

Please refer to the tear-out answer sheet, which is the last page in this booklet, for additional specific completion instructions for this examination. Be sure to read them carefully and to provide all information required on both sides of the answer sheet.

Receiving the Scored Answer Sheet

The Academy scores examination answer sheets with a computerized scoring device and returns them by mail. **Please allow 6 weeks for scoring and return.** At least 150 of the 188 test items (80%) must be answered correctly to pass this examination. Incorrect responses will be noted, but correct answers will not be provided. Students not receiving a passing score will receive a blank answer sheet from the Academy and may attempt the examination again. Those receiving a passing score will receive a letter from the Academy verifying successful completion of *Ophthalmic Medical Assisting: An Independent Study Course.*

Applying for the JCAHPO Certifying Examination

A passing score on this course examination serves as a prerequisite for the written certifying examination for ophthalmic medical assistants offered by the Joint Commission on Allied Health Personnel in Ophthalmology (JCAHPO). Successful completion of this course alone does not constitute certification as an ophthalmic medical assistant.

To register for the JCAHPO examination, students of the Academy's course must request an application form directly from JCAHPO and return it with a copy of their document verifying successful completion of the Academy's course. Full details concerning the application/testing process are included in the examination application packet.

The Academy's letter verifying your successful completion of *Ophthalmic Medical Assisting: An Independent Study Course* is valid for 3 years for JCAHPO application purposes. For more information about the JCAHPO assistant certifying examination or to obtain an application, please contact

Joint Commission on Allied Health Personnel in
 Ophthalmology
2025 Woodlane Drive
St. Paul, MN 55125-2995
Phone: 888-284-3937 or 651-731-2944
Fax: 651-731-0410
e-mail: jcahpo@jcahpo.org
web site: www.jcahpo.org

Chapter 1

1. The only eye care professional who is a medical doctor is the
    a. optometrist
    b. ocularist
    c. ophthalmologist
    d. orthoptist

2. Of the following, the eye care professional who routinely fills prescriptions for eyeglasses is the
    a. ocularist
    b. optician
    c. ophthalmic medical technician
    d. orthoptist

3. A patient in need of a prosthetic eye should be referred to an
    a. ocularist
    b. optician
    c. orthoptist
    d. optometrist

4. An ophthalmologist who concentrates on one area of the eye or focuses on a specific ocular disease is called
    a. an optician
    b. an ocularist
    c. an optometrist
    d. a subspecialist

5. The level directly above certified ophthalmic medical assistant on JCAHPO's certification ladder is
    a. certified ophthalmic medical technologist
    b. certified ophthalmic registered nurse
    c. certified ophthalmic technician
    d. certified ophthalmic photographer

6. Of the following, the responsibility that routinely falls to the ophthalmic medical assistant is
    a. diagnosing certain conditions
    b. making prognostic estimates
    c. performing certain diagnostic tests
    d. prescribing treatment for certain problems

7. An ophthalmic medical assistant accidentally administers too many diagnostic eyedrops to a patient's eye. The first action the assistant should take is to
    a. apologize to the patient and thoroughly wash the eye with water
    b. explain to the patient that the effects of the drops will be intensified
    c. tell the ophthalmologist, who will then decide how to handle the situation
    d. suggest that the patient remain in the office for a while after the examination

8. While waiting for the ophthalmologist, an anxious patient asks the ophthalmic medical assistant for the results of a recent test. The assistant should
    a. explain that the ophthalmologist will discuss these results with the patient shortly
    b. discuss the results with the patient to reduce the level of anxiety
    c. reassure the patient that all is well and that the condition tested is not serious
    d. politely tell the patient that another patient requires attention and leave the room

9. An ophthalmologist's office may disclose information regarding a patient's condition only when the individual seeking the information
    a. is the patient's spouse
    b. has received permission from the patient
    c. is the patient's employer
    d. is a member of the patient's immediate family

Chapter 2

10. Of the following, the structure that is part of the ocular adnexa is the
    a. cornea
    b. eyelid
    c. lens
    d. optic nerve

11. The medial rectus muscle rotates the eye
    a. inward toward the nose
    b. outward toward the temple
    c. downward and inward toward the nose
    d. downward and outward toward the temple

12. The membrane that lines the inner eyelid is the
    a. bulbar conjunctiva
    b. epithelium
    c. palpebral conjunctiva
    d. tarsus

13. The tough, transparent membrane that provides about two thirds of the eye's focusing power is the
    a. retina
    b. conjunctiva
    c. sclera
    d. cornea

14. The white tissue surrounding the cornea and forming the main structural component of the globe is the
    a. ciliary body
    b. limbus
    c. sclera
    d. vitreous

15. The structures of the uveal tract, or uvea, are
    a. iris, ciliary body, choroid
    b. iris, posterior chamber, ciliary body
    c. choroid, sclera, retina
    d. iris, lens, choroid

16. The clear, transparent fluid that fills the anterior chamber is called the
    a. vitreous
    b. aqueous humor
    c. choroid
    d. tear film

17. The condition occurring most often in individuals over age 45 in which the lens can no longer change its shape to focus at near is
    a. accommodation
    b. presbyopia
    c. glaucoma
    d. cataract

18. The primary function of the sphincter and dilator muscles is to
    a. control the amount of light entering the inner part of the eye
    b. raise and lower the eyelid
    c. determine the direction and movement of the eyeball
    d. change the curvature of the lens

19. In this figure of the lacrimal system, the structures are correctly identified as
    a. (1) lacrimal sac (2) punctum (3) lacrimal gland
    b. (1) lacrimal sac (2) nasolacrimal duct (3) lacrimal gland
    c. (1) lacrimal gland (2) punctum (3) lacrimal sac
    d. (1) lacrimal gland (2) lacrimal sac (3) punctum

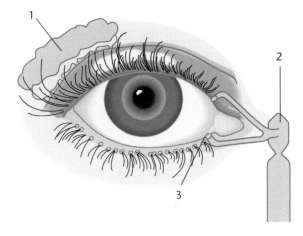

20. Under normal conditions, aqueous fluid leaves the eye in the sequence
    a. trabecular meshwork, through canal of Schlemm, to anterior chamber angle
    b. canal of Schlemm, through trabecular meshwork, to surface blood vessels
    c. anterior chamber angle, through trabecular meshwork, to canal of Schlemm
    d. anterior chamber angle, through surface blood vessels, to trabecular meshwork

21. Injury or degeneration of the macula will most likely result in loss of
    a. night or dim-light vision
    b. peripheral vision
    c. distance vision
    d. detailed central vision

22. In this figure of the visual pathway, the structures are correctly identified as
    a. (1) visual cortex (2) optic tract (3) optic nerve
    b. (1) optic nerve (2) optic chiasm (3) geniculate body
    c. (1) optic chiasm (2) optic tract (3) geniculate body
    d. (1) optic nerve (2) optic chiasm (3) visual cortex

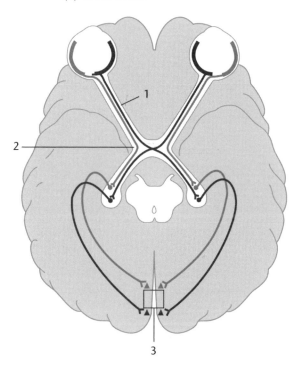

Chapter 3

23. The suffix –*itis* added to the name of a tissue or organ produces the medical term for
    a. infection
    b. inflammation
    c. ischemia
    d. degeneration

24. A body part deprived of its normal blood supply due to a blockage or breakage of a vessel is said to be
    a. inflamed
    b. infected
    c. ischemic
    d. neoplastic

25. Diabetes mellitus is an example of the type of disease process called
    a. metabolic
    b. infectious
    c. neoplastic
    d. degenerative

26. An abnormal change observed by a physician while examining a patient is referred to as
    a. an etiology
    b. a symptom
    c. a sign
    d. a syndrome

27. When the orbital contents swell, pushing the eyeball forward, the resulting condition is termed
    a. blepharitis
    b. exophthalmos (proptosis)
    c. ectropion
    d. exotropia

28. The term *diplopia* is used to describe
    a. swelling from large amounts of fluids
    b. paralysis
    c. double vision
    d. deviation of one or both eyes

29. Treatment of congenital strabismus may include surgery of the
    a. cornea
    b. eyelid
    c. retina
    d. eye muscles

30. Inward deviation of an eye that occurs only when that eye is covered is called
    a. esophoria
    b. esotropia
    c. exophoria
    d. exotropia

31. Amblyopia refers to
    a. the continual movement of the eyes from side to side and up and down
    b. the suppression of visual images from a deviating eye
    c. the abnormal drooping from an upper eyelid
    d. three-dimensional visual perception

32. The term *chalazion* describes
    a. an inward turning of the eyelashes
    b. a drooping upper eyelid
    c. an inflammation of the lacrimal sac
    d. a lump that develops after inflammation and infection of the meibomian glands

33. A condition of dry eyes is called
    a. dacryocystitis
    b. keratoconus
    c. blepharitis
    d. keratoconjunctivitis sicca

34. Primary open-angle glaucoma
    a. is not a threat to vision
    b. can cause permanent damage to the optic nerve
    c. develops rapidly and suddenly
    d. accounts for a small percentage of all glaucomas

35. A cataract is
    a. a clouding of the vitreous gel
    b. a benign growth on the conjunctiva
    c. a branch-shaped corneal ulcer
    d. an opacification of the crystalline lens

36. The appearance of flashes of light in the corner of the eye followed by a sensation of a curtain moving across the vision are symptoms of
    a. age-related macula edema
    b. retinal detachment
    c. retinitis pigmentosa
    d. papilledema

Chapter 4

37. The eyes are considered part of which body system?
    a. endocrine
    b. nervous
    c. respiratory
    d. cardiovascular

38. Which of the following is a waste product of metabolism?
    a. carbon dioxide
    b. oxygen
    c. hemoglobin
    d. hormones

39. Which of the following diseases is a chronic autoimmune condition that interferes with proper nerve transmission in the skeletal muscles?
    a. rheumatoid arthritis
    b. sarcoidosis
    c. myasthenia gravis
    d. Sjögren's syndrome

40. Dry eyes are common in which of the following diseases?
    a. myasthenia gravis
    b. diabetes mellitus
    c. migraine
    d. rheumatoid arthritis

41. The occurrence of blindness among people with diabetes is ___ times that of the general population.
    a. 2
    b. 10
    c. 25
    d. 40

42. The retina examination is often important in detecting which of the following diseases?
    a. hypertension
    b. myasthenia gravis
    c. rheumatoid arthritis
    d. chlamydial infections

43. Acquired immunodeficiency syndrome (AIDS) can cause all of the following eye problems except
    a. cytomegalovirus retinitis
    b. rubella retinitis
    c. Kaposi's sarcoma
    d. herpes zoster ophthalmicus

44. The form of Herpes simplex virus that usually produces genital infections is
    a. type 1
    b. type 2
    c. type 3
    d. type 4

45. Multiple sclerosis frequently presents with
    a. papilledema
    b. infectious retinitis
    c. optic neuritis
    d. anterior uveitis

46. Cancers that produce tumors in more than one part of the body are said to be
    a. radiologic
    b. systemic
    c. metastatic
    d. infective

Chapter 5

47. Substances that permit the passage of light without significant disruption are termed
    a. opaque
    b. transparent
    c. translucent
    d. electromagnetic

48. This figure illustrates the
    a. light-divergent property of a convex lens
    b. light-divergent property of a concave lens
    c. light-convergent property of a convex lens
    d. light-convergent property of a concave lens

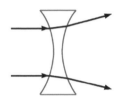

49. A convex lens with a focal length of 0.50 meter has a power of
    a. 0.20 D
    b. 0.50 D
    c. 2.00 D
    d. 5.00 D

50. This figure shows the focal point of light rays in an eye that is
    a. myopic
    b. presbyopic
    c. emmetropic
    d. hyperopic

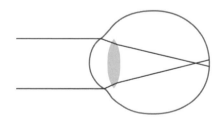

51. A toric cornea is characteristic of
    a. hyperopia
    b. myopia
    c. presbyopia
    d. astigmatism

52. The type of lens that best corrects myopia combined with astigmatism is a
    a. cylindrical lens
    b. spherical lens
    c. spherocylindrical lens
    d. multifocal lens

53. The difference between the power of the upper segment and the power of the lower segment in a bifocal lens is referred to as the
    a. circle of least confusion
    b. refractive index
    c. principal meridian
    d. add

54. The correct transposition of the plus-cylinder prescription $+100 +200 \times 90$ to its minus-cylinder form is
    a. $+300 -200 \times 90$
    b. $+100 -200 \times 180$
    c. $+300 -200 \times 180$
    d. $+200 -100 \times 90$

55. The term *neutralization* in retinoscopy refers to
    a. administering cycloplegic eyedrops, which block accommodation
    b. finding the lens power that affects movement of the retinal reflex and fills the pupil with light
    c. measuring the prescription of the patient's existing eyeglasses
    d. balancing the correction of both the patient's eyes

56. If the distance portion of an eyeglass lens is +2.00 D and the bifocal add is +1.00, then the bifocal power is
    a. +1.00 D
    b. +2.00 D
    c. +3.00 D
    d. −1.00 D

57. The first step in performing manual lensometry or keratometry is to
    a. focus the eyepiece
    b. lubricate the instrument
    c. position the eyeglasses
    d. position the patient

58. If the lensmeter mires cannot be centered in the central portion of the lensmeter target, the lens probably contains a
    a. sphere
    b. cylinder
    c. spherocylinder
    d. prism

Chapter 6

59. One disadvantage of ophthalmic medicinal ointments is that they
    a. may cause unwanted effects in other parts of the body
    b. may blur vision when applied
    c. cannot be used in patients with excessive tearing
    d. do not remain in contact with the eye surface for very long

60. Of the following, the type of injection classified as a form of systemic drug delivery is the
    a. intravitreal
    b. subconjunctival
    c. subcutaneous
    d. retrobulbar

61. When instilling eyedrops, the ophthalmic medical assistant should
    a. administer the medication directly onto the cornea
    b. make certain the dropper makes contact with the conjunctival sac
    c. administer the medication directly into the conjunctival sac
    d. apply indirect pressure to the eyelids

62. Of the following, the drug that is most helpful when performing both a fundus examination and an objective refraction on a pediatric patient is
    a. an anesthetic
    b. a miotic
    c. a mydriatic
    d. a cycloplegic

63. The two types of drugs that could stimulate an attack of angle-closure glaucoma in patients with narrow anterior chamber angles are
    a. mydriatics and cycloplegics
    b. mydriatics and antihistamines
    c. anesthetics and dyes
    d. antiallergic and anti-inflammatory agents

64. In ophthalmology, topical anesthetics are most often used to
    a. perform major eye surgery
    b. treat cornea defects on a long-term basis
    c. relieve minor eye fatigue and redness
    d. prevent discomfort during diagnostic procedures

65. Miotics function to reduce intraocular pressure by
    a. decreasing the production of aqueous humor
    b. contracting the ciliary body muscle and opening the outflow channels for aqueous humor
    c. paralyzing the ciliary body muscle and closing the anterior chamber angle
    d. dilating the pupil and opening the anterior chamber angle

66. All of the following are used to treat bacterial infections except
    a. neomycin
    b. sulfonamides
    c. nystatin
    d. bacitracin

67. The topical drug phenylephrine is classified as
    a. a miotic
    b. a mydriatic
    c. an anesthetic
    d. an antimicrobial

68. The ophthalmologist has written a prescription that includes the abbreviations "gtt" and "bid." These indicate that the prescribed drug is
    a. an ointment to be administered every hour
    b. an ointment to be administered at bedtime
    c. topical drops to be administered 4 times a day
    d. topical drops to be administered twice a day

69. Topical corticosteroids function primarily as
    a. lubricants, which keep the external eye moist and maintain the tear film balance
    b. antimicrobials, which inhibit the growth of bacteria, viruses, or fungi
    c. irrigating solutions, which flush out the eye during surgical procedures
    d. anti-inflammatory and antiallergic agents, which reduce swelling and scarring of the lids and anterior segment

70. A common side effect of cycloplegics is
    a. eye redness
    b. blurred vision
    c. high blood pressure
    d. corneal edema

Chapter 7

71. The microbe most likely to cause recurrent fever blisters is
    a. adenovirus
    b. cytomegalovirus
    c. Epstein-Barr virus
    d. herpesvirus

72. A corneal abrasion caused by a tree twig is most likely to cause a
    a. fungal infection
    b. protozoal infection
    c. viral infection
    d. chlamydial infection

73. Of the following, the people most at risk for developing an ocular infection by the protozoan *Acanthamoeba* are those who
    a. eat undercooked or raw meat
    b. use homemade salt solutions to clean their contact lenses
    c. have had chickenpox during childhood
    d. use contaminated cosmetics

74. The primary purpose of standard precautions is to
    a. identify disease-causing microbes
    b. reduce the opportunity for harmful microbes to flourish and threaten patients and medical personnel
    c. protect the sterility of a sterilized article
    d. destroy all microorganisms in the office environment

75. A tonometer tip is best disinfected by using
    a. boiling water
    b. moist heat
    c. a germicide
    d. soap and water

76. Sterilization is best defined as
    a. the transmission of infectious microbes from reservoir to host
    b. the range of procedures used to prevent the spread of infectious microbes in the office
    c. the process of inactivating or eliminating most disease-causing microorganisms
    d. the destruction of all microorganisms

77. An autoclave is used to
    a. disinfect medical materials that would be destroyed by dry or moist heat
    b. sterilize medical materials by means of pressurized moist heat
    c. sterilize medical materials by means of dry heat
    d. decontaminate reusable medical materials before they are sterilized

78. If the ophthalmic medical assistant accidentally touches the sterile functional surface of a disposable instrument, the instrument should be
    a. resterilized in the office
    b. wiped with alcohol
    c. wiped with a sterile cloth
    d. discarded, no matter what its cost

79. An infection caused when the eye has been penetrated by a contaminated metal fragment is an example of
    a. direct-contact transmission
    b. indirect-contact transmission
    c. common-vehicle transmission
    d. vector transmission

80. Ophthalmic medical assistants with open cuts on their hands
    a. should wear gloves to protect patients
    b. should wear gloves to protect themselves
    c. should wear gloves to protect both patients and themselves
    d. do not need to wear gloves if they wash their hands before and after working with patients

Chapter 8

81. What part of the comprehensive medical eye examination includes the inspection of the visible parts of the lacrimal apparatus?
    a. ophthalmoscopy
    b. the external examination
    c. the alignment and motility examination
    d. the visual field examination

82. Healthy, asymptomatic individuals between the ages of 40 and 64 should have a comprehensive medical eye examination every
    a. 6 months
    b. year
    c. 2 to 4 years
    d. 5 years

83. When recording the patient's chief complaint, the ophthalmic medical assistant should
    a. include an evaluation of the patient's condition
    b. substitute technical terms for the patient's words
    c. include only the facts as stated by the patient
    d. include any diagnoses that seem likely

84. Close examination of the lids, lashes, cornea, and lens can be accomplished with the
    a. biomicroscope
    b. ophthalmoscope
    c. gonioscope
    d. exophthalmometer

85. In the Snellen acuity recording 20/100, the number 100 represents the
    a. size of the largest optotype seen by the patient
    b. distance in feet from the patient to the chart
    c. distance in meters from the patient to the chart
    d. distance in feet at which a normal eye can see a particular line on the chart

86. If a pinhole acuity test is found to significantly improve a patient's poor visual acuity, the patient probably has
    a. glaucoma
    b. a cataract
    c. poor peripheral vision
    d. a refractive error

87. Jaeger notations, Snellen M units, and distance equivalents are various units of measuring
    a. near visual acuity
    b. ocular motility
    c. peripheral vision
    d. pupil width

88. Having a patient follow a finger in the six cardinal positions of gaze is a method of evaluating
    a. direct pupillary reaction
    b. peripheral vision
    c. extraocular muscle function
    d. distance acuity

89. The prism and alternate cover test is used to
    a. evaluate depth perception
    b. evaluate peripheral vision
    c. measure deviation in a misaligned eye
    d. measure near visual acuity

90. Of the following, the procedure that must be performed before pupillary dilation is
    a. cycloplegic refraction
    b. biomicroscopy
    c. ophthalmoscopy
    d. the swinging-light test

91. In a normal consensual reaction, when a light is directed into the pupil of one eye, the pupil of the other eye
    a. constricts
    b. dilates
    c. is unchanged
    d. pulsates

92. Of the following, the test that evaluates disturbances or defects in the visual field is the
    a. Worth four-dot test
    b. Titmus stereopsis test
    c. Schirmer test
    d. Amsler grid test

93. Intraocular pressure is measured by flattening a small area of the central cornea in
    a. keratometry
    b. applanation tonometry
    c. indentation tonometry
    d. Schiøtz tonometry

94. A reading of 3 on the Goldmann tonometer dial indicates an intraocular pressure of
    a. 0.3 mm Hg
    b. 3 mm Hg
    c. 15 mm Hg
    d. 30 mm Hg

95. Gonioscopy is a procedure used to view the
    a. external structures of the eye
    b. structures of the anterior chamber angle
    c. vitreous
    d. optic nerve head

96. Indirect ophthalmoscopy provides a
    a. nonmagnified view of the fundus
    b. 15-fold magnified view of the fundus
    c. wider field of view of the fundus than does direct ophthalmoscopy
    d. narrower field of view of the fundus than does direct ophthalmoscopy

Chapter 9

97. The three transparent structures that compose what is termed the ocular media are the
    a. cornea, lens, and retina
    b. conjunctiva, cornea, and lens
    c. cornea, lens, and vitreous
    d. lens, vitreous, and aqueous humor

98. The interferometer measures visual acuity potential by using a laser or special light beams to
    a. project parallel lines onto the macula
    b. photograph the cornea's endothelial cells
    c. project a lighted Snellen chart onto the retina
    d. deliver radiating sound waves throughout the cornea

99. Pachymetry is useful in determining the
    a. position and size of tumors within the eye
    b. macular function in a patient with a media opacity
    c. degree of a patient's sensitivity to glare
    d. ability of the cornea to withstand the stress of surgery

100. Of the following, the procedure used for counting endothelial cells of the cornea is
    a. fluorescein angiography
    b. specular microscopy/photography
    c. ultrasonography
    d. pachymetry

101. An acuity chart printed in faint gray rather than in sharp black on white is useful for measuring
    a. near visual acuity
    b. glare sensitivity
    c. color vision
    d. contrast sensitivity

102. Fluorescein angiography is a valuable method of detecting and documenting
    a. abnormalities in the structure of the outer eye
    b. corneal endothelial cells
    c. abnormalities in ocular blood vessels
    d. lens opacities

103. Of the following, the procedure most useful in calculating the power of an artificial lens to be implanted in a patient who has undergone cataract extraction is
    a. A-scan ultrasonography
    b. B-scan ultrasonography
    c. fluorescein angiography
    d. specular microscopy

Chapter 10

104. The printed circles on a visual field chart refer to the
    a. radial meridians
    b. boundaries of a normal patient's island of vision
    c. circles of eccentricity at 10° intervals
    d. holes within the contour of an otherwise normal visual field

105. On a visual field chart, in kinetic perimetry, a contour obtained with a single target of a particular size and brightness is
    a. shallow scotoma
    b. an absolute scotoma
    c. an isopter
    d. a circle of eccentricity

106. Generally, the 0° point on visual field charts of both the right and the left eye is located at the
    a. extreme right on the horizontal meridian, and the other meridians are measured progressively in a clockwise direction
    b. extreme left on the horizontal meridian, and the other meridians are measured progressively in a clockwise direction
    c. extreme right on the horizontal meridian, and the other meridians are measured progressively in a counterclockwise direction
    d. top of the vertical meridian, and the other meridians are measured progressively in a counterclockwise direction

107. A defect in the inferior temporal retina will affect the
    a. inferior temporal field of vision
    b. inferior nasal field of vision
    c. superior temporal field of vision
    d. superior nasal field of vision

108. On visual field charts, the physiologic blind spot appears in the
   a. center of the visual field
   b. nasal visual field
   c. temporal visual field
   d. inferior visual field

109. Two examples of static perimetry are
   a. the tangent screen test and the contrast sensitivity test
   b. suprathreshold perimetry and Autoplot perimetry
   c. the tangent screen test and Goldmann perimetry
   d. threshold perimetry and suprathreshold perimetry

110. The technique of placing a target of a given size in the visual field and gradually increasing its brightness until the patient sees it is the basis for
   a. threshold perimetry
   b. suprathreshold perimetry
   c. the tangent screen test
   d. Goldmann perimetry

111. One disadvantage of Goldmann perimetry is that it
   a. covers only the central 30° of the visual field
   b. requires the examiner to move the target at the same speed in each direction
   c. provides no means of controlling the brightness of test targets
   d. produces printed results that are difficult to plot and interpret

112. One advantage of the computerized threshold perimetry is that it
   a. is quicker and easier to perform than kinetic perimetry
   b. is more sensitive in detecting shallow defects than kinetic perimetry
   c. eliminates the need for the technician to remain in the room
   d. eliminates the need for patient response

113. In this visual field chart of the right eye, the arrow on the left points to an area of decreased visual sensitivity known as a
   a. physiologic blind spot
   b. scotoma
   c. depression
   d. hemianopia

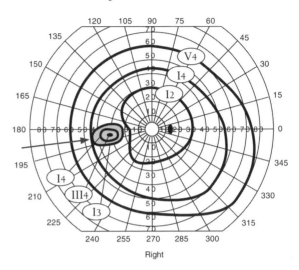

Right

114. In this visual field chart of both eyes, the condition depicted is most often due to
   a. glaucoma
   b. small pupil size
   c. a lesion or tumor in the optic chiasm
   d. cataracts

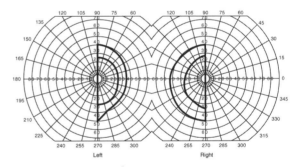

Left   Right

115. For accurate perimetry, the patient's near correction must be in place if the patient
   a. has ptosis
   b. is presbyopic
   c. has a pupil size of 2 mm or smaller
   d. is easily distracted

Chapter 11

116. Correction for distance, near, and intermediate division in one lens can be achieved with
    a. an executive bifocal lens
    b. a round-top segment bifocal lens
    c. a single-vision lens
    d. a double-D segment trifocal lens

117. Transitional zones or areas of bleeding that create distorted or blurred vision are a particular drawback of
    a. round-top multifocal lenses
    b. conventional seamed multifocal lens
    c. progressive-addition multifocal lenses
    d. polarized lenses

118. Because of its resistance to shattering, the material of choice for safety lenses is
    a. heat-treated flint glass
    b. chemically treated flint glass
    c. CR-39
    d. polycarbonate

119. Interpupillary distance is measured principally to determine
    a. the base curve of a lens
    b. the optical center of a lens
    c. the pantoscopic angle of a lens frame
    d. the segment height of a multifocal lens

120. Interpupillary distance is the distance from the
    a. temporal limbus of one pupil to the temporal limbus of the other pupil
    b. center of one pupil to the center of the other pupil
    c. center of one pupil to the bridge of the nose
    d. nasal limbus of one pupil to the bridge of the nose

121. The procedure for obtaining monocular interpupillary distance involves measuring the distance from
    a. one pupil to the other in a single measurement
    b. the temporal limbus of one eye to the nasal limbus of the other eye
    c. one pupil to the bridge of the nose and then multiplying the result by 2
    d. each pupil to the bridge of the nose separately and then adding the results

122. The accurate measurement of vertex distance during refractometry is required
    a. for all refractive prescriptions
    b. only for multifocal prescriptions
    c. only for prescriptions with corrections greater than or equal to –5 or +5 D
    d. only for prescriptions with corrections less than or equal to –5 or +5 D

123. As a starting point, most opticians recommend fitting the top of a bifocal segment
    a. level with the upper lid margin
    b. level with the lower lid margin
    c. level with the lower rim of the pupil
    d. exactly at the middle of the eyeglass lens

Chapter 12

124. The contact lenses that allow oxygen to reach the cornea only through the tear pump are
    a. soft lenses
    b. rigid gas-permeable lenses
    c. polymethylmethacrylate lenses
    d. extended-wear lenses

125. A prescription for contact lenses
    a. is identical to that for eyeglasses
    b. requires only keratometry and refraction measurements
    c. includes both keratometry and base curve measurements
    d. includes vertex and interpupillary distance measurements

126. One significant advantage of soft lenses over rigid gas-permeable lenses is that soft lenses
    a. generally are easier to handle, clean, and disinfect
    b. can correct large amounts of astigmatism or irregular corneas more effectively
    c. generally are easier to adapt to and initially more comfortable to wear
    d. can be modified after manufacture

127. An allergic reaction related to contact lens wear is most often due to the individual's sensitivity to a
    a. soft contact lens material
    b. rigid contact lens material, such as silicone acrylate
    c. soap used to wash hands before insertion
    d. preservative or disinfectant chemical in a lens solution

128. Cosmetic restorative lenses are most appropriate for patients who
    a. want to enhance or change the color of their irises
    b. have disfigured eyes
    c. require relief from photophobia or glare sensitivity
    d. have large amounts of astigmatism that would otherwise require thick glasses

129. Disinfection of contact lenses serves primarily to
    a. remove surface protein deposits
    b. keep the lens surface hydrophilic
    c. prevent the growth of bacteria, viruses, and fungi
    d. lubricate the area between the cornea and the lens

130. Contact lenses are most likely to be contraindicated in individuals who
    a. have refractive errors resulting from keratoconus
    b. work in occupations requiring excellent peripheral vision
    c. participate heavily in sports activities
    d. are routinely exposed to excessive amounts of fumes or dust

131. Generally, when inserting a soft contact lens on a patient, the ophthalmic medical assistant should first place the lens on the
    a. sclera above the cornea
    b. sclera below the cornea
    c. sclera to the right or left of the cornea
    d. cornea directly

132. A corneal abrasion caused by foreign material lodged between the cornea and the contact lens
    a. can result in a serous corneal infection
    b. usually is more painful in soft lens wearers than in rigid lens wearers
    c. usually requires no treatment beyond removal of the lens for a few days
    d. always requires treatment with a pressure patch

133. The only acceptable rinsing solution for contact lenses is
    a. salt tablets dissolved in distilled water
    b. salt tables dissolved in tap water
    c. the contact lens user's own saliva
    d. sterile saline solution

Chapter 13

134. The primary purpose of triage is to
    a. obtain the patient's complete ophthalmic history
    b. diagnose the patient's problems
    c. classify the patient's chief complaint according to its severity and urgency
    d. schedule office appointments according to the availability of the physician

135. If the ophthalmic medical assistant notices a discrepancy between a patient's report of a traumatic injury and the injury itself, the assistant should
    a. confront the injured patient immediately
    b. inform the ophthalmologist in private, without the patient present
    c. inform the ophthalmologist in the presence of the patient
    d. disregard the discrepancy, as this matter is not the responsibility of the ophthalmic medical assistant

136. Of the following, the situation that should be treated as an emergency requiring immediate action is a
    a. recent onset of flashes of light
    b. loss of contact lenses needed for work
    c. mucous discharge from the eye
    d. sudden, painless, severe loss of vision

137. Generally, urgent situations are those requiring that the patient be seen within
    a. 3 to 6 hours
    b. 24 to 48 hours
    c. 5 to 7 days
    d. 1 to 2 weeks

138. A patient telephones the ophthalmologist's office reporting an alkali burn in the eye. The ophthalmic assistant should instruct the patient to
    a. patch the eye and proceed immediately to the office or emergency facility
    b. keep the eye closed and proceed immediately to the office or emergency facility
    c. irrigate the eye with water for 20 minutes and then proceed to the office or emergency facility
    d. put a lubricating ointment on the eye and proceed immediately to the office or emergency facility

139. When assisting a patient who feels faint in the office, the ophthalmic medical assistant should first
    a. begin cardiopulmonary resuscitation (CPR)
    b. get the emergency chart
    c. splash water on the patient's face
    d. get the patient's head below the heart

Chapter 14

140. In encounters with irate or hostile patients, the best approach an ophthalmic medical assistant can take is to
    a. recommend that they see another physician
    b. try to convince them that they are being unreasonable
    c. listen calmly to their complaints and apologize for any misunderstanding
    d. ignore them until they calm down

141. When interacting with a visually impaired or blind patient, the ophthalmic medical assistant should
    a. approach quietly to avoid startling the patient
    b. speak through an accompanying companion
    c. speak loudly to ensure comprehension
    d. face the patient and say the patient's name

142. A papoose board is useful in
    a. propping up a toddler at the slit lamp
    b. immobilizing an infant during an ophthalmic evaluation
    c. transporting a toddler from one examining room to another
    d. testing visual acuity in a school-age child who cannot identify letters

143. The "fix and follow" method of evaluating visual function is generally used with
    a. infants
    b. school-age children
    c. elderly patients
    d. patients with low vision

144. A patient with insulin-dependent diabetes suddenly becomes sweaty, dizzy, and disoriented while waiting to see the ophthalmologist. The assistant, acting in compliance with the office's emergency procedures, should first
    a. reschedule the appointment and send the patient home
    b. have the patient lie down until the episode passes
    c. give the patient fruit juice or candy to stabilize the blood sugar level
    d. have the patient drink one or two glasses of water

145. When testing visual acuity in elderly patients, the ophthalmic medical assistant should
    a. concentrate on distance acuity, as near acuity is not important in this age group
    b. require that these patients respond quickly, so that an objective measurement can be obtained
    c. adjust the lighting to avoid glare, which often is a problem in this age group
    d. use the Allen chart rather than the Snellen chart when testing distance acuity

146. Approximately 95% of all individuals over age 65 have some degree of
    a. glaucoma
    b. cataract
    c. diabetes
    d. diplopia

147. When the ophthalmic medical assistant schedules a lengthy appointment for a patient with insulin-dependent diabetes, the most appropriate recommendation to make to the patient is to
    a. fast for several hours before the appointment
    b. come in right before lunch
    c. come in right after breakfast or lunch
    d. eat lightly on the day of the appointment

148. When the ophthalmic medical assistant asks a literate 8-year-old patient to read the visual acuity chart, the child begins reciting the alphabet. The most effective action the assistant can take to get the test results needed is to
    a. praise the child for trying hard to cooperate
    b. ask the parent to get the child started reading the chart
    c. ask the child to start at the beginning of the chart and say each letter separately
    d. move the child closer to the chart

Chapter 15

149. Of the following, the task that is the responsibility of the ophthalmic medical assistant when caring for a patient undergoing minor surgery is
    a. initiating the discussion of informed consent
    b. prepping the patient for the procedure
    c. administering a local anesthetic by injection
    d. determining when the patient is steady enough to leave the office

150. The discussion involved in obtaining informed consent
    a. is necessary only before a major surgical procedure
    b. occurs between the patient and the ophthalmic medical assistant
    c. covers the benefits as well as the risks of the procedure
    d. is conducted mainly for the protection of the surgeon

151. Of the following, the suture material that is not broken down by the body but must be removed from the suture site is
    a. polypropylene
    b. collagen
    c. gut
    d. polyglactin 910

152. The rhomboid-shaped needle point used in procedures involving the cornea or sclera, where the plane of penetration must be precise, is the
    a. cutting point
    b. reverse-cutting point
    c. spatula point
    d. taper point

153. In this photograph, the surgical instruments are correctly identified from left to right as
    a. scissors, forceps, needle holder
    b. forceps, scissors, needle holder
    c. needle holder, forceps, scissors
    d. forceps, needle holder, scissors

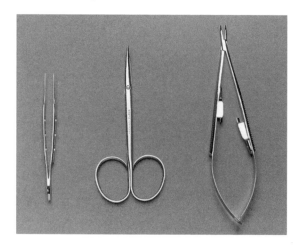

154. To maintain hemostasis during a surgical procedure, the surgeon uses
    a. curettes
    b. cannulas
    c. clamps
    d. forceps

155. In lacrimal-system probing, a cannula is used to
    a. enlarge the small punctal opening
    b. scoop out unwanted tissue
    c. hold the suture needle steady
    d. flush out a tear duct with an irrigating solution

156. All of the following are considered to be within the sterile operating field except
    a. the instrument tray
    b. masks
    c. gloves
    d. drapes

157. Prepping the patient is usually done
    a. after the final scrubbing and without sterile gloves
    b. before final scrubbing and without sterile gloves
    c. after final scrubbing and with nonsterile gloves
    d. before final scrubbing and with sterile gloves

158. Of the following, the suture size least likely to be used for eye surgery is
    a. 2–0
    b. 5–0
    c. 8–0
    d. 10–0

Chapter 16

159. Which of the following refractive techniques is reversible?
    a. LASIK
    b. LASEK
    c. conductive keratoplasty
    d. intracorneal ring segments

160. Contraindications to refractive surgery include all of the following except
    a. contact lens-induced corneal warpage
    b. progressive myopia
    c. glaucoma
    d. corneal ectasia

161. In the absence of accommodation, the myopic eye focuses images
    a. in front of the retina
    b. behind the retina
    c. in front of the lens
    d. on the sclera

162. Hyperopic eyes are benefited by refractive procedures that
    a. dilate the pupil
    b. steepen the cornea
    c. decrease the power of the crystalline lens
    d. decrease the corneal thickness

163. Intracorneal ring segments are used to treat all of the following except
    a. early keratoconus
    b. low levels of myopia
    c. low levels of hyperopia
    d. ectasia after LASIK surgery

164. One limitation of cycloplegia in the preoperative refractive surgery evaluation is
    a. distortion of image
    b. relaxation of accommodation
    c. dilation of pupil
    d. production of spherical aberrations

165. In PRK, the laser is applied to
    a. Bowman's layer
    b. anterior stroma
    c. mid-stroma
    d. Descemet's layer

166. Wavefront error measurement is called
    a. keratometry
    b. pachymetry
    c. aberrometry
    d. videokeratography

167. Significant haze occurs in LASIK when
    a. the epithelium is accidentally ablated
    b. the flap is too thin
    c. the flap is too thick
    d. the crystalline lens is removed

168. Disadvantages of LASIK include all of the following except
    a. flap malpositions
    b. microkeratome malfunction
    c. increased corneal astigmatism
    d. reduction of corneal stability

Chapter 17

169. Which of the following technician behaviors is not appropriate?
    a. determining why the patient is visiting the office
    b. reviewing patient appointment lists with the doctor
    c. discussing clinical findings with the patient
    d. discussing clinical findings with the doctor

170. All of the following are measures of clinical productivity except
    a. number of follow-up appointments
    b. number of visits per lane per hour
    c. revenue generated per patient visit
    d. number of new and established patient visits

171. External causes of injury and poisoning are described by
    a. V codes
    b. E codes
    c. A codes
    d. D codes

172. OSHA prescribes how practices protect
    a. patient privacy
    b. patients against fraudulent billing
    c. employee health and safety
    d. employee coding practices

173. The standard method by which diagnoses are reported is
    a. ICD
    b. CPT
    c. E & M
    d. OMA

174. Appropriate code linking requires
    a. ICD–9 codes
    b. national standards
    c. counseling
    d. medical necessity

175. The key components used to determine the appropriate level of E & M code include all of the following, except
    a. history
    b. diagnosis
    c. examination
    d. medical decision-making

176. Documentation standards for E & M services are recognized
    a. on a practice basis
    b. on an insurance basis
    c. on a national carrier basis
    d. on a diagnostic basis

177. The ICD-9-CM lists all of the following factors influencing a patient's condition except
    a. illnesses
    b. symptoms
    c. medications
    d. injuries

178. Do not code
    a. a "suspected" diagnosis
    b. symptoms
    c. signs
    d. history of present illness

Chapter 18

179. Which of the following is not a handheld instrument?
    a. Tono-Pen
    b. direct ophthalmoscope
    c. indirect ophthalmoscope
    d. retinoscope

180. All of the following lenses do not contact the eye except a
    a. Koeppe lens
    b. Hruby lens
    c. condensing lens
    d. handheld fundus lens

181. How often should authorized maintenance service be scheduled for the phoropter?
    a. monthly
    b. every 6 months
    c. yearly
    d. every 2 years

182. The lensmeter unit includes all of the following components except
    a. focusing eyepiece
    b. prism bar
    c. lens holder
    d. light source

183. The keratometer measures the curvature of the central ____ mm of the anterior corneal surface in its two meridians.
    a. 2.3
    b. 2.7
    c. 3.3
    d. 3.7

184. To clean the tonometer tip, wipe it with
    a. saline
    b. acetone
    c. soap and water
    d. alcohol

185. The instrument that is used to examine the entire retina in stereopsis is
    a. the indirect ophthalmoscope
    b. the direct ophthalmoscope
    c. the retinoscope
    d. the Hruby lens

186. The potential acuity meter is used to determine potential visual acuity in patients with
    a. cataracts
    b. diabetes
    c. glaucoma
    d. strabismus

187. Lenses that contact the eye should be disinfected with
    a. a 10% solution of acetone for 5 minutes
    b. a 10% solution of acetone for 10 minutes
    c. a 1:10 dilution of bleach and water for 5 minutes
    d. a 2% aqueous solution of glutaraldehyde for 5 minutes

188. If an electrical instrument fails to work, the technician should check all of the following except
    a. is the instrument plugged into an outlet?
    b. has the instrument overheated?
    c. is the bulb burned out?
    d. are the central wall outlet and electrical fuse for the circuit functioning?